The Big Book

of

Easter

Written by Helen Hall

Published by Prim-Ed Publishing

The Big Book of Easter

Written by Helen Hall
Foreword

James Aiton Primary School
Morriston Street
Cambuslang
Glasgow
G72 7HZ

This book has been published for use in lower primary Years and is a bumper edition of fun activities and worksheets that can be integrated into the teaching program as a complete theme or as individual activities.

Activities cover the language, mathematics, creative and problem-solving aspects of the school program and can be adapted to suit the requirements of different ages.

Contents

Easter Ideas

Maths
Area, Tangrams
Measurement, Space
Maze
Addition, Subtraction
Problem Solving
Ordering
Counting on
Game and puzzle

Art/Crafts
Puppets - Hen and Rabbit
Masks - Hen and Rabbit
Easter baskets
Paper folding/cutting
Weaving
Easter cards
Colouring

Language
Brainstorm Easter words
Tell/Read about the first Easter
Read *The Easter Story* on page 1
Make a scroll about Easter
Write a paragraph about each
picture

Reading
The Easter Story
The Easter Rabbit
What am I?

Comprehension
Questions
Jumbled sentences
Read and draw

Word Study
Sleuths
Alphabetical order
Make words
Rhyming words
Jumbled words
Contractions
Blend activity
Digraph activity
Secret message

The Easter Story

All His life Jesus had been kind and good to everyone. He loved the little children and helped the sick people. However, His enemies hated Him because He said He was the Son of God and would be their King.

One night as He prayed in the Garden of Gethsemane, His enemies captured Him. Jesus did not try to escape. In the morning they took Him to Pontius Pilate, the ruler of the land. Pontius Pilate could not find anything that Jesus had done wrong. But the people shouted out to Pilate 'Crucify Him! Crucify Him!'.

The Crucifixion

The soldiers whipped Jesus and tore His clothes and made Him wear a crown of thorns. Pilate told the soldiers to take Jesus away and crucify Him. He was made to carry the cross until He became very weak. Then Simon, a man in the crowd, was ordered by the soldiers to carry the cross for Him. He was led to the hill called Calvary (Golgotha), near Jerusalem, and there they nailed His hands and feet to the wooden cross.

As Jesus hung on the cross He prayed for His enemies. Many people laughed and shouted at Him to save Himself but Jesus did not answer. Jesus died on the cross. His work on Earth had finished. He had died for the sins of the people.

That night some of Jesus' friends came and took His body down. They wrapped Him in some clean cloth and put Him in a grave. A large stone was rolled in front of the tomb. They were very sad because their friend was dead.

The Resurrection

On the first Easter morning some women went to the garden where the body of Jesus had been put in a tomb. To their surprise the rock had been rolled away and the tomb was open. The body of Jesus was gone.

The women ran quickly to tell the disciples what they had found. On the way, to their amazement, they met Jesus. They fell down and worshipped Him. Jesus said, 'Don't be afraid but go and tell all my friends that you have seen me'.

That evening they all met in a room in the town. They were so happy because some of them had seen Jesus alive. Suddenly, Jesus was in the room with them. At first they thought He was a ghost, but Jesus showed them His hands and feet. Now the friends knew that He was really alive and they were glad.

After that Jesus appeared before many people until it was time to arise and go to His Father in Heaven.

The Bible tells us that Jesus is living and that He is the Son of God. He wants us to love Him and follow the path that He has shown us in His teachings.

Questions

1. Who was Jesus?

   _____

   _____

2. Why was Jesus hated by many people?

   _____

   _____

3. What was the name of the ruler of the land?

   _____

4. How did they kill Jesus?

   _____

   _____

5. Where did Jesus' friends put His body?

   _____

   _____

6. Why do you think they put a rock in front of the tomb?

   _____

   _____

7. Where did Jesus go after He was resurrected?

   _____

   _____

Easter Scroll

Colour the pictures on the next two pages then cut and glue them together on the dotted lines. Glue the two ends onto two cardboard tubes and wind the story around so that the first picture is shown. Write a paragraph about each picture and glue it to the back.

Read your story and turn the scroll.

The soldiers capture Jesus in the Garden of Gethsemane.

Pontius Pilate sentences Jesus to death.

Jesus walks to the Hill of Calvary (Golgotha).

Jesus dies on the cross.

Jesus is alive again.

The Easter Rabbit

1. Photocopy pages 6 and 7 back to back. 2. Cut and fold to make an Easter book.

I am the Easter Rabbit.
I hop from place to place.

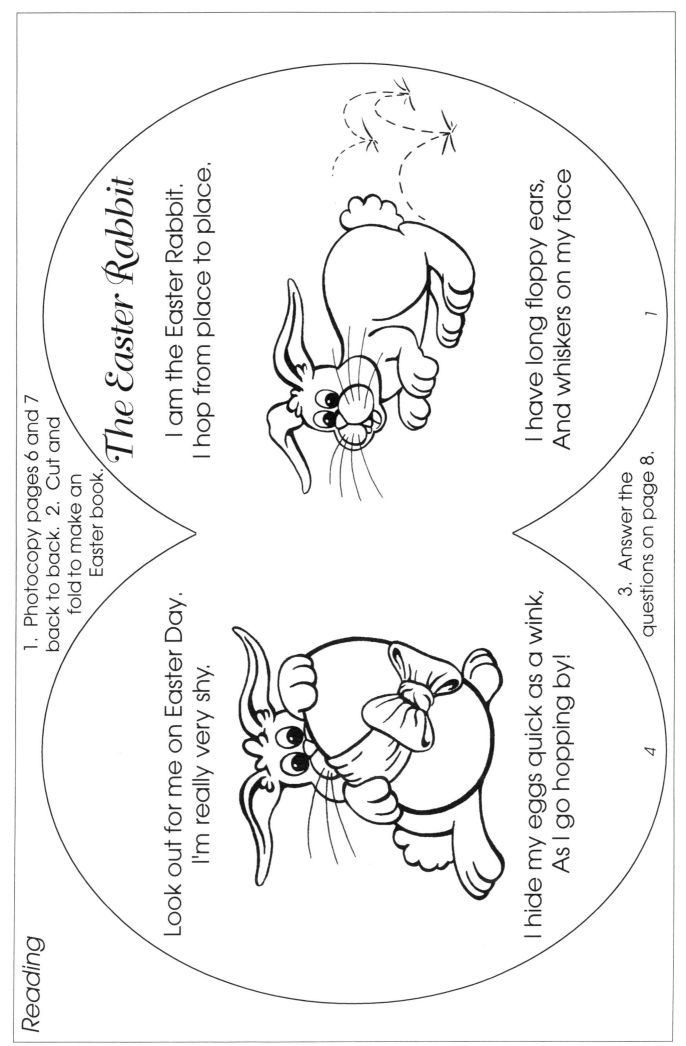

I have long floppy ears,
And whiskers on my face

1

Look out for me on Easter Day.
I'm really very shy.

4

I hide my eggs quick as a wink,
As I go hopping by!

3. Answer the questions on page 8.

Can you see my basket?
It's full of Easter treats.

Some are made of chocolate.
Some are full of sweets.

3

My tail is white and fluffy.
My nose is soft and pink.

I'm a friendly little bunny.
I know that's what you think.

2

Rhyming Words

Read the poem *The Easter Rabbit*.

Find pairs of rhyming words.

For example: place   face

_____ _____

_____ _____

_____ _____

_____ _____

Unjumble these poem words.

bibrat _____   stwsee _____

resa _____   tbskea _____

gegs _____   nikp _____

artEes _____   uyo _____

yfulff _____   seon _____

nybun _____   lait _____

Contractions

I'm   = _____

I'll   = _____

that's = _____

it's   = _____

can't = _____

Read, Draw and Colour.

Here is the Easter bunny.
Make his nose pink.
Colour his tail yellow.
Colour his coat red and blue.
Draw a green bowtie with black dots.
Put three coloured eggs in his basket.
Draw two blue birds in the sky.
Draw a bright yellow sun.

Easter Jumble

Unjumble these sentences.

cross Jesus the on Easter died at time.

_____

during We hot eat buns Easter. cross

_____

Easter The brings children. rabbit Easter for eggs

_____

made chocolate. Easter be eggs can of

_____

Pancakes eat. to are delicious

_____

Make as many words as you can from the word
CHOCOLATE

1. tool   2. _____
3. _____   4. _____
5. _____   6. _____
7. _____   8. _____
9. _____   10. _____
11. _____   12. _____
13. _____   14. _____
15. _____   16. _____

Picture Crossword

Use the picture clues to complete the crossword.

Across

1.

2.

4.

6.

8.

Down

1.

3.

5.

E _ _ _ _ _

7.

9.

Alphabetical Order

Write these words in alphabetical order.

Easter   rabbit   chicken   egg   Jesus   life   God
cross   chocolate   crown   love   death

_____

_____

_____

_____

Make as many words as you can from the word

E A S T E R

1. rest
2. _____
3. _____
4. _____
5. _____
6. _____
7. _____
8. _____
9. _____
10. _____
11. _____
12. _____
13. _____
14. _____
15. _____
16. _____

Put these words into sentences.
1. Easter, eggs, rabbit
2. chocolate, basket, treats
3. love, Jesus

Word Study

Cut out the cross and the blend strip below. Cut along the dotted lines on the cross. Insert the blend strip. Sound out the 'cr' words. List them in your pad and illustrate them.

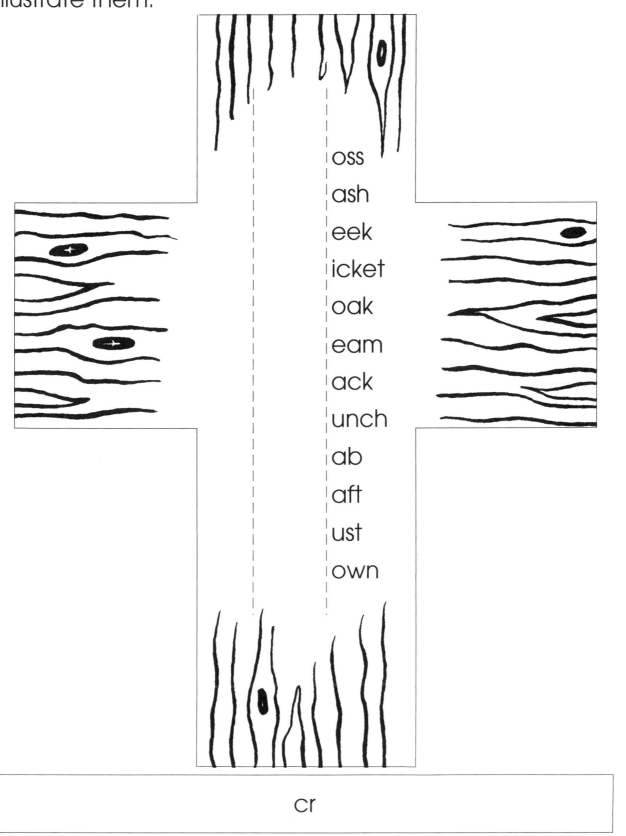

oss
ash
eek
icket
oak
eam
ack
unch
ab
aft
ust
own

cr

Word Study

Cut out the Easter Bunny and the digraph strip below.
Cut along the dotted lines. Insert the digraph strip.
Sound out the 'ea' words. Write them in a sentence.

ster

m	t
l	f
p	ch
r	ch
b	ch
t	ch
cl	n
sp	k

ea

Easter Sleuth

Circle these words.

Jesus cross Jerusalem palms cave tomb sin
heaven God crown thorns worship disciples

Words read

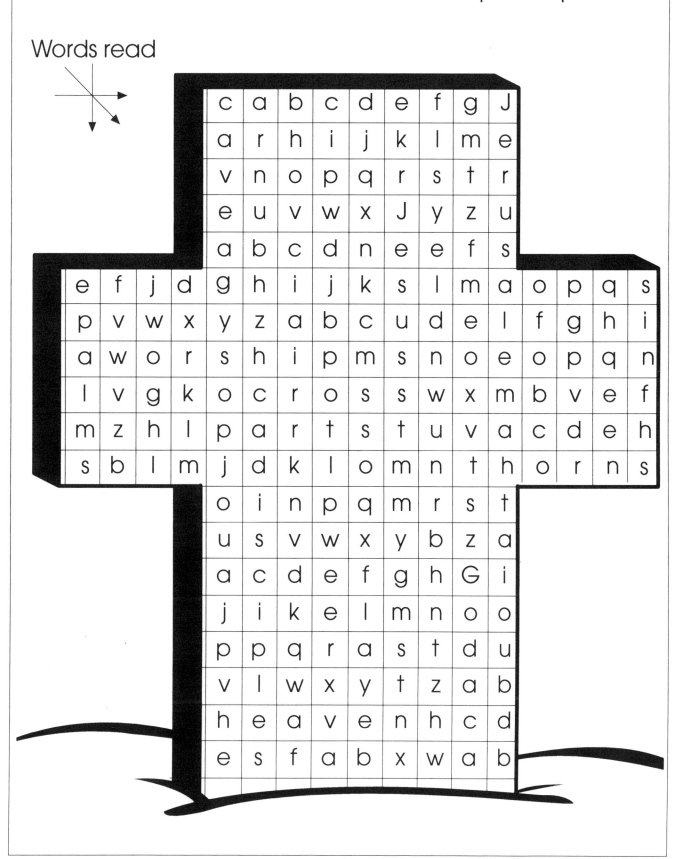

Easter Sleuth

Circle these words.

chocolate fluffy flowers
birds festival family
marshmallows

friends party lambs rabbits
lolly Easter eggs bunny

Words read

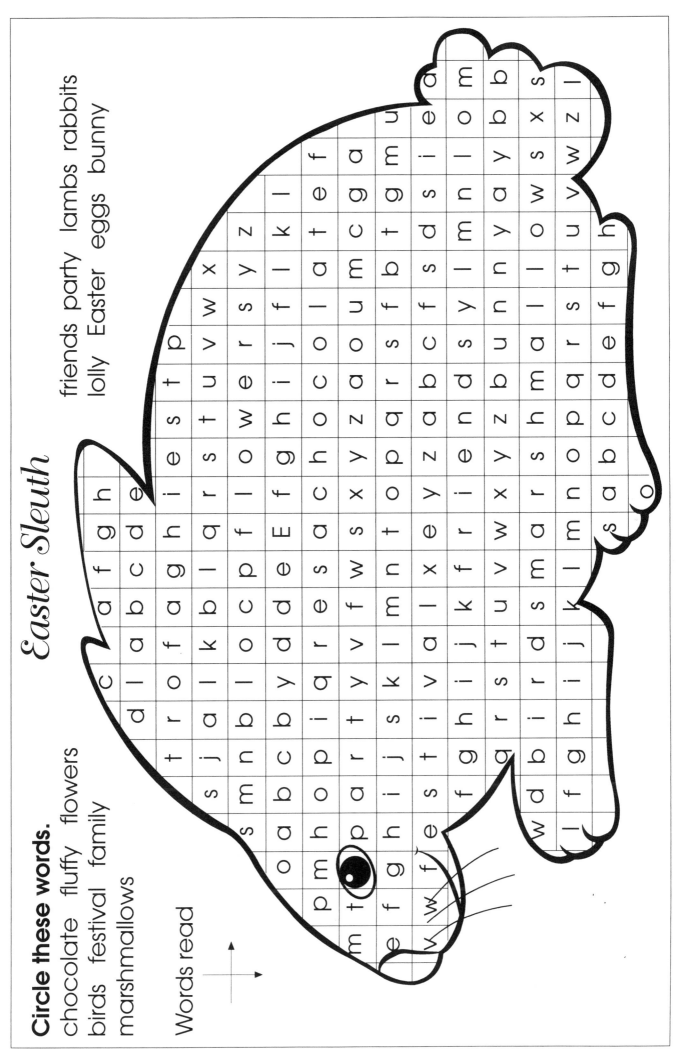

Easter Sleuth

Circle these words.

chicken hen lay rooster hatch mate nest
incubator warm soft fluffy peck eggs shells
cheep basket

Words read

Acrostic Poem

Write an Easter acrostic poem.

E _____

A _____

S _____

T _____

E _____

R _____

An Easter Story

What Will the Easter Bunny Bring You for Easter?

Write about the Real Meaning of Easter

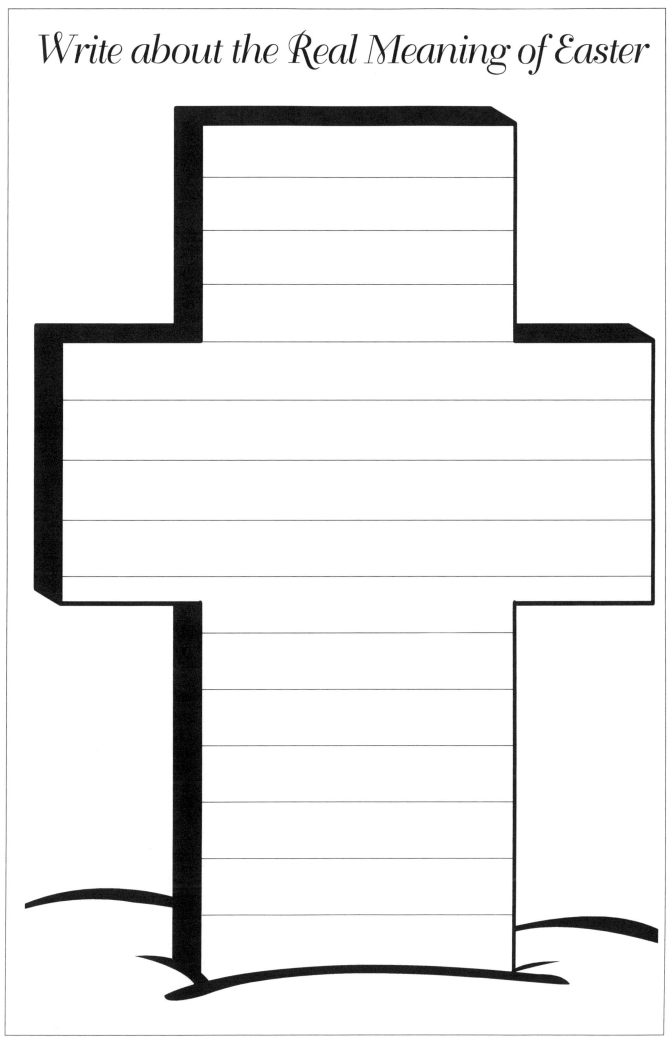

Easter Brings New Life

Fill this Egg with Easter Words

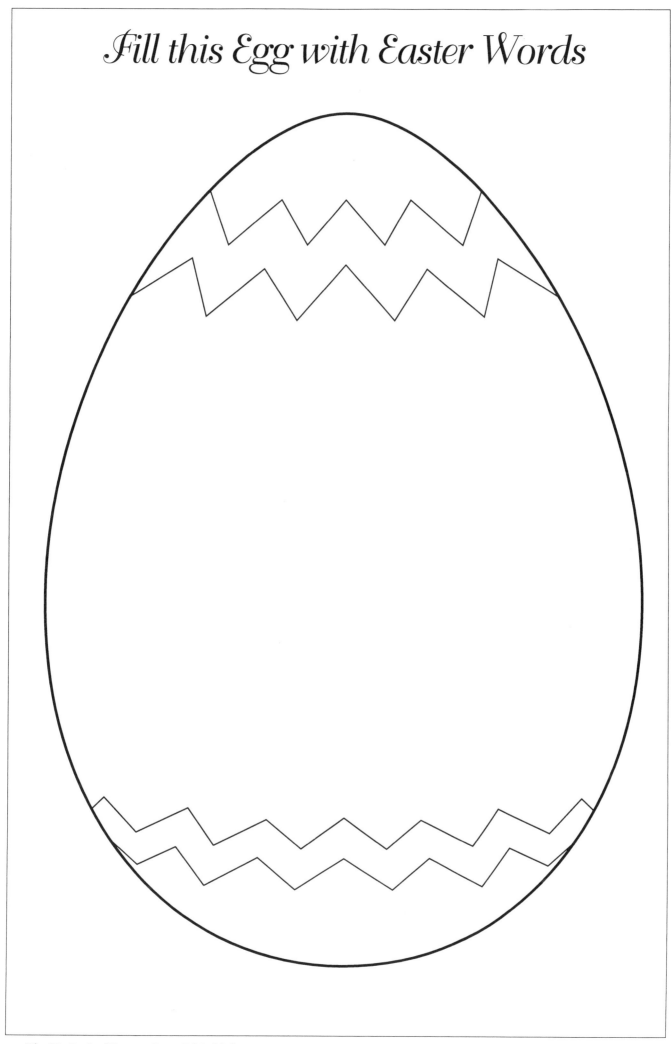

How Many Easter Eggs Can You Eat?

$\square + 3 = 14$

$\square + 3 + 3 = 15$

$\square + 8 = 8$

$\square + 9 = 9$

$\square + 2 = 8$

$9 + \square = 12$

$5 + \square = 15$

$8 + \square = 12$

$\square + 4 = 7$

$1 + \square = 9$

$\square + 8 = 14$

$\square + 0 = 7$

$\square + 5 + 5 = 10$

$4 + \square = 10$

$\square + 3 = 11$

$7 + \square = 10$

$1 + \square = 9$

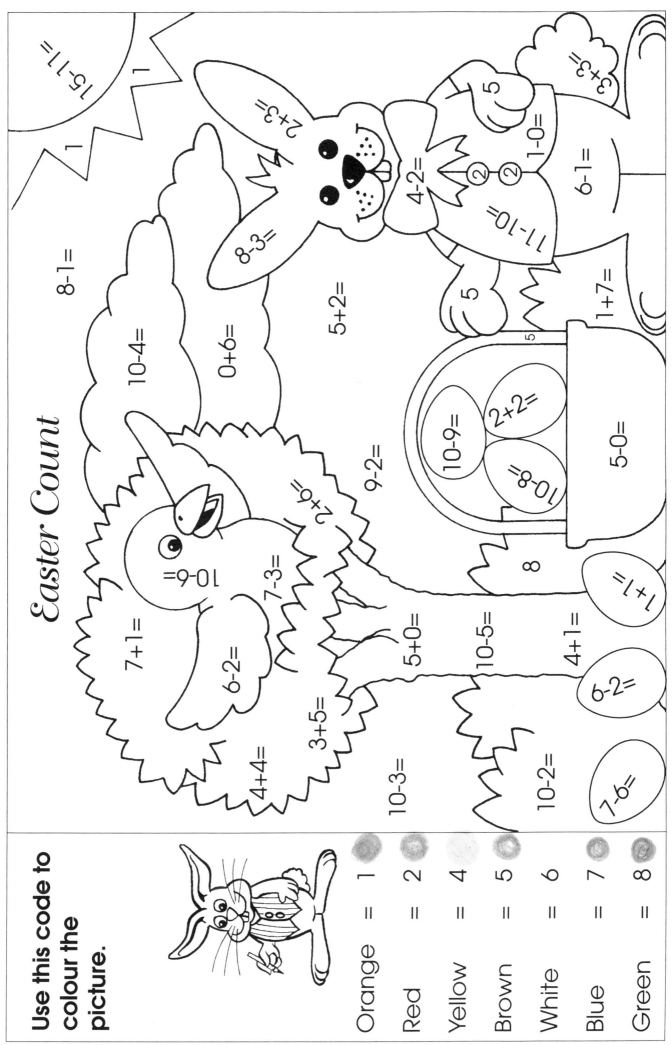

Easter Count

Use this code to colour the picture.

Orange	=	1
Red	=	2
Yellow	=	4
Brown	=	5
White	=	6
Blue	=	7
Green	=	8

Equations in the picture:

15-1=
1
1
2+3=
8-3=
3+3=
5
1-0=
4-2=
2 2
11-10=
6-1=
8-1=
10-4=
0+6=
5+2=
5
1+7=
5-0=
10-9=
2+2=
10-8=
9-2=
2+6=
10-6=
7+1=
7-3=
6-2=
3+5=
4+4=
10-3=
5+0=
8
10-5=
4+1=
10-2=
1+1=
6-2=
7-6=

Easter Chick

Cut out the shapes below and arrange them to make an Easter chick.
Graph the shapes you used by colouring the bar graph on page 27.

Easter Chick Graph

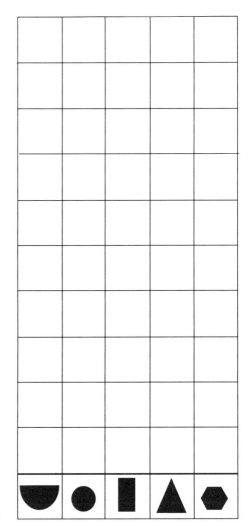

Graph the shapes used to make your chick.

Which shape was used the most?

_____

Which shape was used the least?

_____

How many circles did you use?

_____

How many triangles did you use?

_____

How many circles and hexagons did you use altogether?

_____

Did you use more rectangles than hexagons? _____

Join the dots.

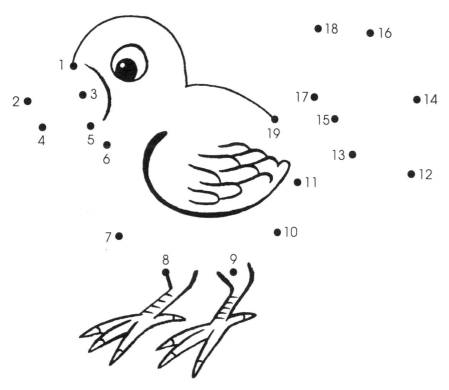

Help the Easter Bunny to Deliver the Easter Eggs

Easter Pictures

Copy these pictures onto the grids.

Count the squares you use.

Can you double the size of each picture on another grid?

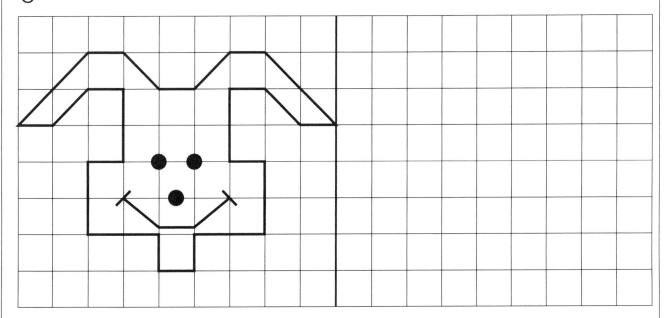

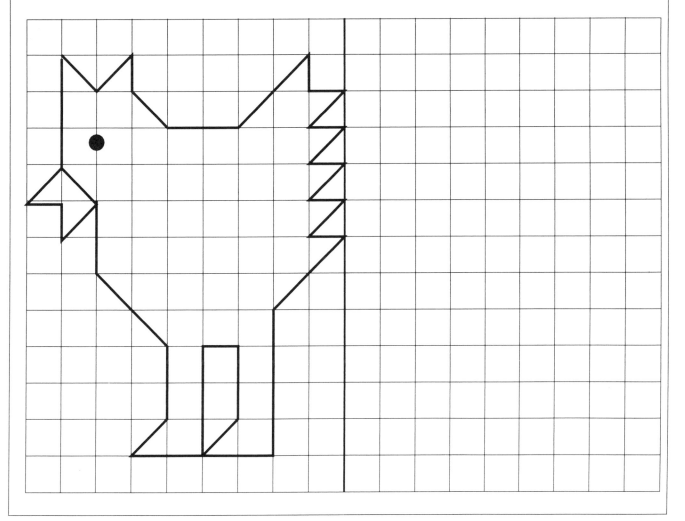

Secret Code

Find out the Easter message using the code below.

A	B	C	D	E	F	G	H	I	J	K	L	M
1	2	3	4	5	6	7	8	9	10	11	12	13

N	O	P	Q	R	S	T	U	V	W	X	Y	Z
14	15	16	17	18	19	20	21	22	23	24	25	26

9   8 15 16 5   20 8 5   5 1 19 20 5 18

___   ___ ___ ___ ___   ___ ___ ___   ___ ___ ___ ___ ___ ___

2 21 14 14 25   2 18 9 14 7 19   25 15 21

___ ___ ___ ___ ___   ___ ___ ___ ___ ___ ___   ___ ___ ___

12 15 20 19   15 6   5 7 7 19

___ ___ ___ ___   ___ ___   ___ ___ ___ ___.

8 1 16 16 25   5 1 19 20 5 18

___ ___ ___ ___ ___   ___ ___ ___ ___ ___ ___!

Write your own secret message using the code.

Bunny Bounce

Who will be first to bounce his or her bunny home?

Rules: You need one die, bunny tokens and egg cards from page 32.

1. Throw a six to start.
2. Take turns.
3. If you land on an egg, pick up a card and follow the instructions.

Bounce, Bunny, Bounce!

START

FINISH

Bunny Bounce

Photocopy onto card and cut out.
Colour the tokens and pictures.

Tokens

Egg cards

Good bouncing. Bounce forward 2 spaces.	Good bouncing. Bounce forward 3 spaces.	Good bouncing. Bounce forward 4 spaces.	Good bouncing. Bounce forward 1 space.
Dropped the eggs. Miss a turn.	Dropped the eggs. Miss a turn.	Dropped the eggs. Miss a turn.	Dropped the eggs. Miss a turn.
Stopped for a nap. Throw a six.	Met a friend. Throw a six.	Take cover from rain. Throw a six.	Lost your way. Throw a six.
Happy days! Take another turn.	Sun smile! Bounce an extra space.	Keep smiling! Go forward two bounces.	Feeling sunny! Bounce forward two spaces.
We love Easter. Take another turn.	Nearly there! Bounce an extra square.	Sore feet! Miss a turn.	Stop for tea. Miss a turn.

An Easter Puzzle

Cut out the nine pieces.
Rearrange them to make the picture.

Easter Bunny Problem

Each Easter Bunny needs a coloured coat and bowtie. Their coats can be red, blue or yellow. Their bowties are green, orange or purple. No two bunnies are the same.
How many different coloured bunnies can you colour?

Easter Eggs

Decorate and colour the eggs.
Cut out the eggs and order them from smallest to tallest.

Easter Fun

Look at this bunny. Use the code to colour him.

○ = yellow   □ = blue   △ = brown   ⬡ = black   ▭ = red

How many circles? _____   How many squares? _____

How many hexagons? _____   How many triangles? _____

How many rectangles? _____

Circle the answer.

Easter Bunny's head is a circle/rectangle.

Easter Bunny's tail is a square/hexagon.

Easter Bunny's ears are squares/triangles.

Easter Bunny's tummy is a circle/hexagon.

Tangram Rabbit

Cut out the tangram. Rearrange the shapes to make this rabbit. Can you make any other animals?

Tangram Chicken

Cut out the tangram. Rearrange the shapes to make this chicken. Try to make other tangram animals.

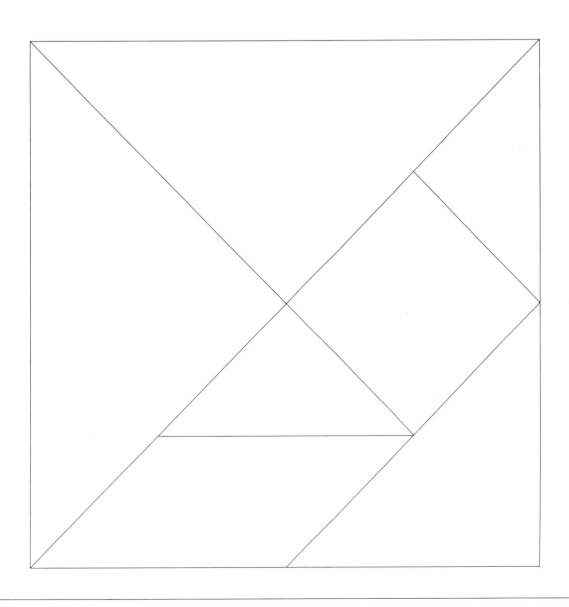

Area

Copy the word 'Jesus' onto the grid below. Answer the questions on the following page.

Area

Look at the word JESUS on the grid on page 39.

1. How many squares does the letter E cover? _____

2. How many squares does the letter J cover? _____

3. How many squares does the word JESUS cover altogether? _____

4. Which letter covers the most squares? _____

5. Does the letter S cover more or less squares than the letter E? _____

6. Does the letter U cover more or less squares than the letter J? _____

Try to write the word LOVE on the grid below. How many squares does your word cover? _____

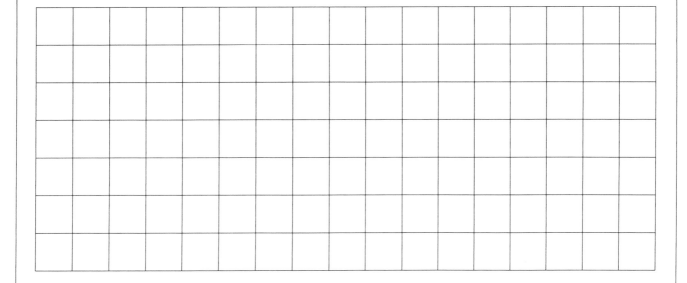

Estimate and Measure

Estimate, then measure each bunny with your ruler.
Answer the questions on page 42.

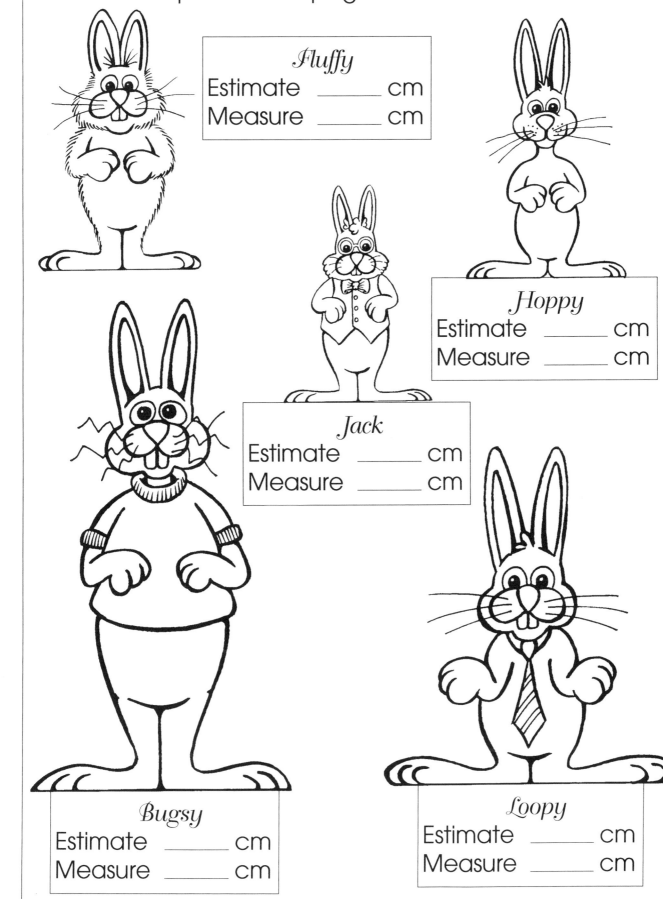

Fluffy
Estimate _____ cm
Measure _____ cm

Hoppy
Estimate _____ cm
Measure _____ cm

Jack
Estimate _____ cm
Measure _____ cm

Bugsy
Estimate _____ cm
Measure _____ cm

Loopy
Estimate _____ cm
Measure _____ cm

Estimate and Measure

Using your bunnies from page 41, complete the graph.

Height

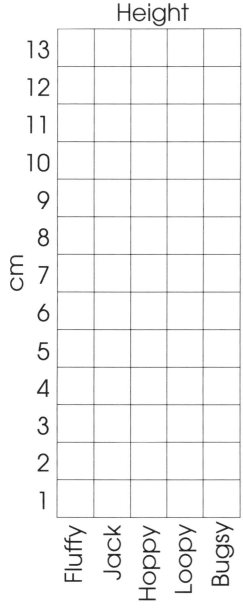

cm — 13, 12, 11, 10, 9, 8, 7, 6, 5, 4, 3, 2, 1

Fluffy Jack Hoppy Loopy Bugsy

1. Which bunny is the tallest?

   _____

2. Which bunny is the shortest?

   _____

3. Are any bunnies the same height? _____

4. How tall is the second tallest bunny? _____cm

5. What is the difference in height between the tallest and shortest bunny?

   _____cm

6. Find the difference in height between the second tallest and the tallest bunny.

   _____ cm

Easter Colouring

Easter Hen Puppet

1. Cover a cardboard tube with coloured paper.
2. Colour and cut out the hen's body parts.
3. Glue the body parts onto the cardboard tube.

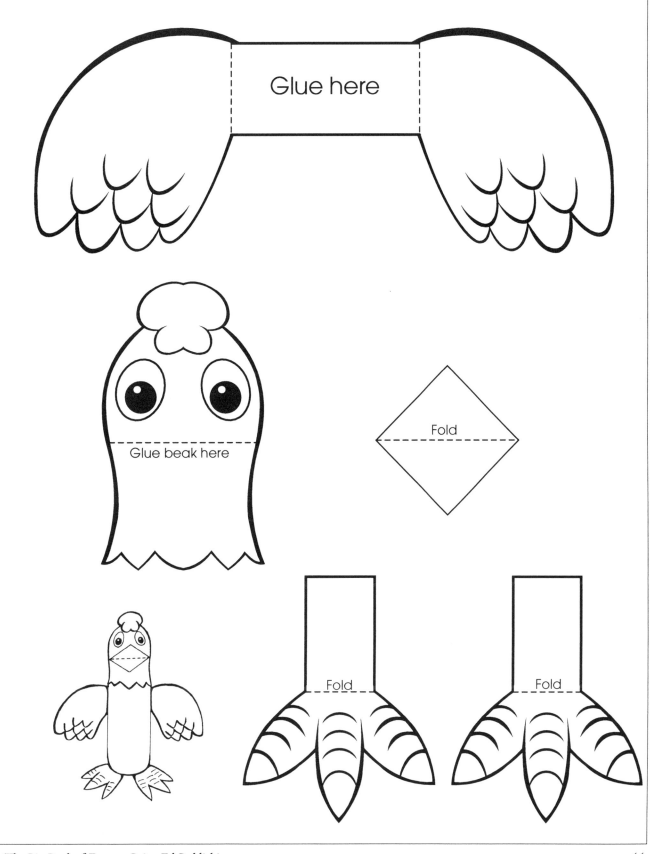

Glue here

Glue beak here

Fold

Fold

Fold

Easter Bunny Puppet

Colour and cut out the rectangle. Glue the rectangle around a cardboard tube. Colour and cut out the bunny's head and feet.

Glue the head, feet and a cotton ball tail to the cardboard tube body.

Glue here

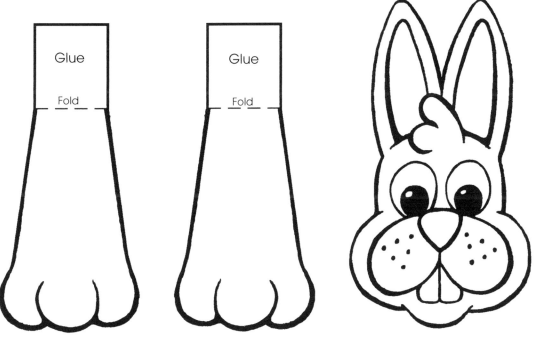

Glue

Fold

Glue

Fold

Easter Bunny Mask

Colour and cut out the mask below. Cut out the eye holes. Attach strings at the sides.

Cheeping Chicken

1. Colour and cut out the chicken face and eye holes.
2. Fold vertically in half with the face inside.
3. Cut the mouth line and fold back the triangles.
4. Open the triangles and face and push the triangles forward so that they open on the inside.
5. Move the sides of the face to make the chicken cheep.

Easter Card

1. Colour and cut out the card.
2. Fold side pieces.
3. Write a message on the inside and decorate.

HAPPY

EASTER

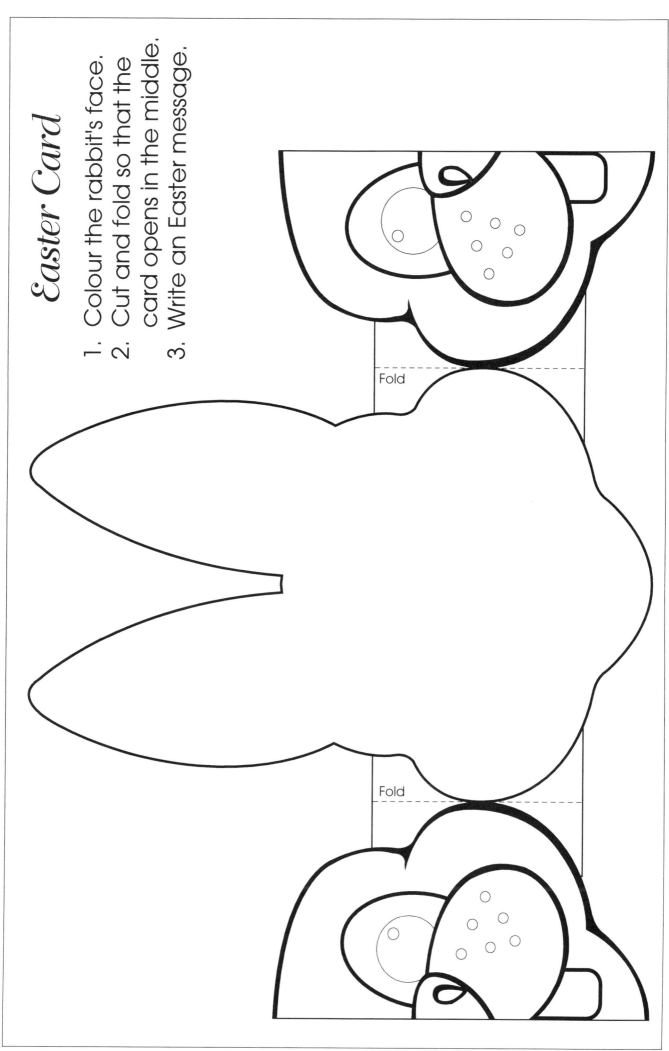

Easter Card

1. Colour the rabbit's face.
2. Cut and fold so that the card opens in the middle.
3. Write an Easter message.

Fold

Fold

What am I?

What am I?

1. Photocopy page 51 back to back with this page.

2. Cut out the egg shape.

I am a chick
I am a soft chick.
I am a fluffy chick.
Look at me!

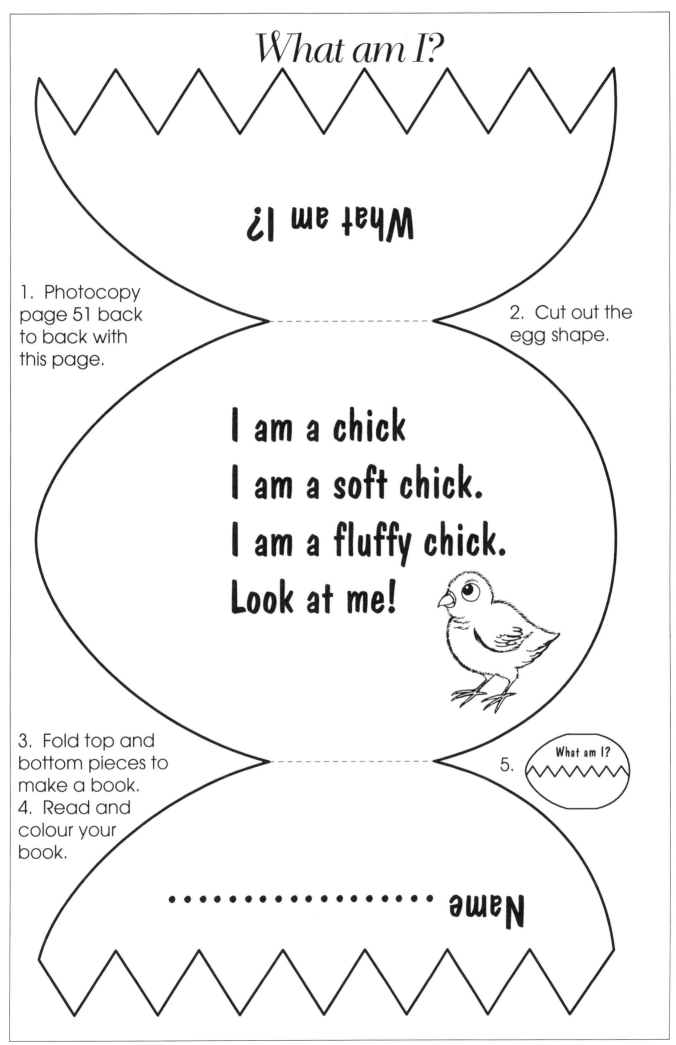

3. Fold top and bottom pieces to make a book.
4. Read and colour your book.

5. What am I?

• Name

Look at me!
I am yellow.
I am fluffy.

I can walk.
I can run.
I can eat.
Can I hop?
No! I can't hop!

Look at my feather.
It is soft.
It is fluffy.

Chicken Weaving

1. Colour the chicken body parts. Contrasting colours are more effective.
2. Cut out the two pieces.
3. Cut along the dotted lines.
4. Carefully weave one part to the other. Glue ends.

Bouncing Bunny

1. Colour the rabbit's face and feet.
2. Cut out the rabbit.
3. Fold along dotted line.

4. Carefully cut the lines on the rabbit's body.
5. Open carefully and stretch a little.
6. Bounce your rabbit.

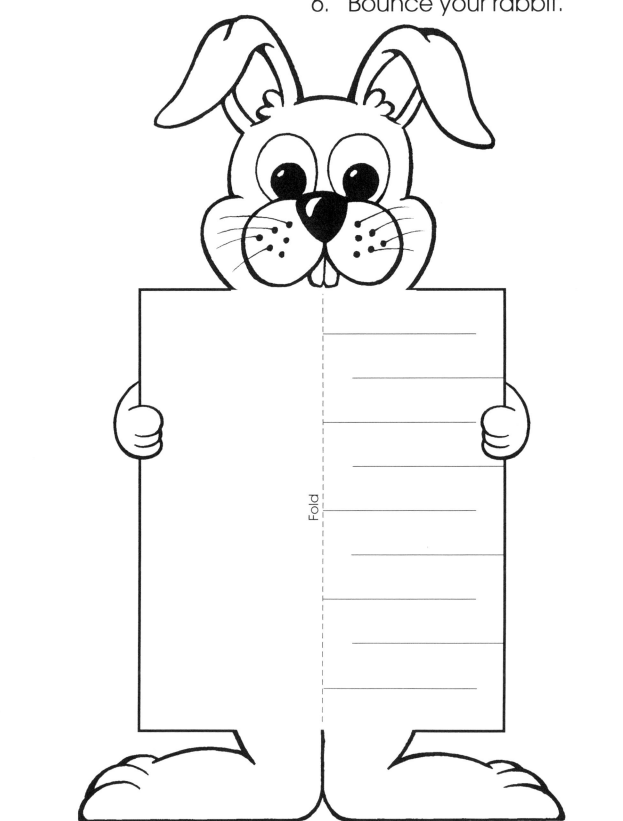

Fold

Chicken in a Basket

1. Colour and cut out the basket and handle.
   (Remember to only cut the outside of the chicken.)
2. Fold up on dotted lines.   3. Glue the sides.
4. Staple on the handle.   5. Fill with Easter treats.

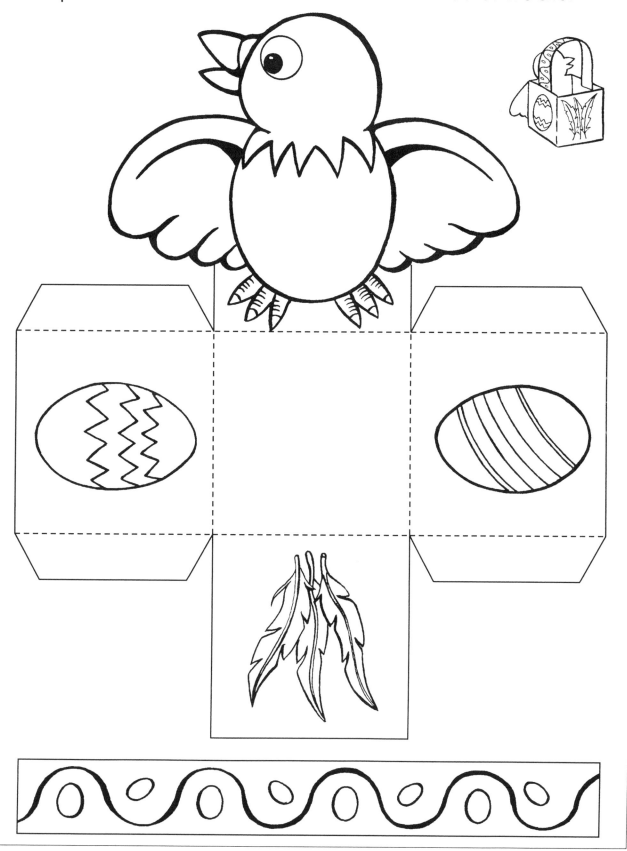

Easter Basket

1. Colour and cut out the basket and handle.
2. Fold on dotted lines.   3.   Glue the sides.
4. Staple on the handle.
5. Glue on a cotton ball for a tail.
6. Fill with Easter treats.

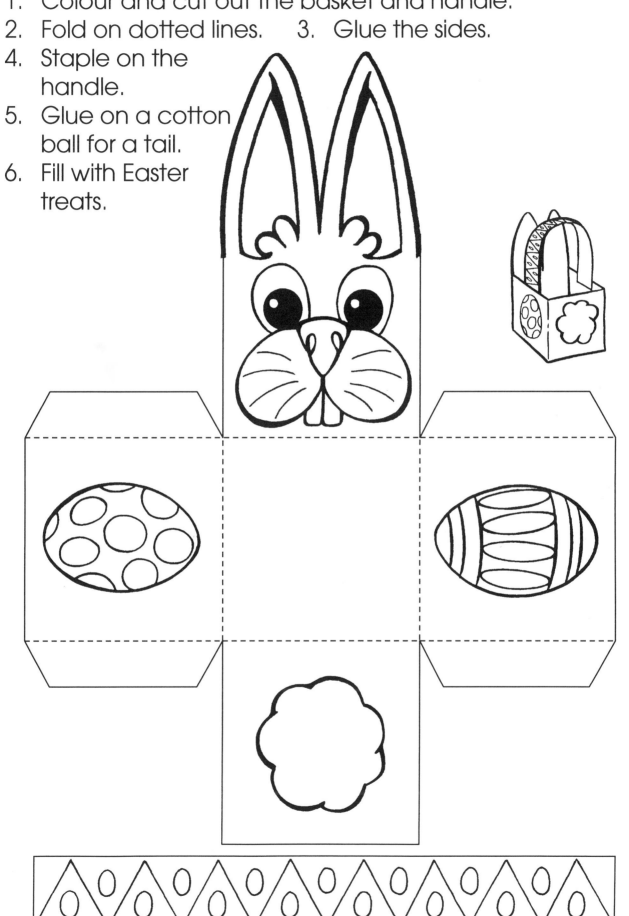